Dad got flowers for Mum.

He had a big bunch.

"Flowers for Mum," he said.

He put the flowers on the back.

"Lost flowers," said her mum.
She put them on a bin.

Dad was in a rush.

He had lost the flowers.

Wilma saw the flowers.

The flowers fell off.

Oh no! Dad was upset.

He went back to the flower
shop.

He got a big bunch of flowers.

Dad saw his lost flowers.
"Well, well," he said.

"Flowers for Mum," said Dad.

"Mix them up," said Chip.
"Then it will be a big bunch."

"It's an enormous bunch"
said Mum. "Thank you."